✦ 111MAGIC LIST ✦
JOURNAL

by

Joanna Hunter

www.joannahunter.com

@joannahuntercom

ISBN 978-0-9933027-7-0
First Edition 2022 - Paperback/Hardback
Authored by Joanna Hunter
Cover Image by Jennifer Hughes
Cover Design by Joanna & Paul Hunter
Formatting by Jennifer Hughes
Published by My Inner Peace Publishing

Dedication

I dedicate this journal to my children & all the magic seekers of this world.

My hope is that you will know that you are worthy of living your dreams out loud and of creating lives that light your soul on fire. May you always know that you are loved and meant for all the more your heart desires.

Introduction to

✦ 111MAGIC LIST ✦

Get excited because what you have in your hands in the form of this 111Magic Journal is a legit conduit to magic!!! This is one of my favourite ways to create with energy.

The magic in this journal is twofold, but before I explain let me introduce myself. I am Joanna Hunter, an author, spiritual channel, teacher, and the High Priestess of the LightWeb, a soul-based technology that will change your life! I live in the magical Highlands of Scotland, surrounded by nature, family, and magic! I am the founder of www.joannahunter.com.

I live a manifested life, a life I created with my own intentions, which I then spoke and wrote into being, which is now my reality. I weaved my life with my magic. Teaching others to do the same is my passion in life.

My spirit team Skylar, a collective consciousness that I channel, teaches that we are all sacred creators and has shared 13 powerful insights with me, called the BeMagic Insights, to help us remember and reactivate our creator power within. BeMagic Insight two simply states:

"Language is the first magic humans learn. Words are the gatekeepers of energy"

I love this insight. Working with it, I have learned to wield the magic of words, and bespell my life in the most incredible way that has allowed me to manifest my dreams into reality. I've also had the pleasure of seeing hundreds of clients do the same.

For word magic to be its most potent, I follow these 3 rules:

1. Radical self-honesty. Be honest with yourself. Tell it like it is. Don't dream of a Fiat when you really want a Porsche. Even if you have no clue how you will manifest a Porsche, for example, own your desire for it. There is magic in the ownership of desire.

2. Let it harm none. You reap what you sow. Do not sow rotten seeds like revenge, anger, and jealousy. Sow from pure intentions, like love, desire, and joy.

3. Get Selfish. Your dream should first and foremost be about you, then filter outward. If all your dreams are about other people's joy or helping them, as noble as that sounds, it is very disempowering energy to yourself and them. They have their own sacred creator power and free will to dream their own dreams. If you wish to know more about this read my book 'Get Selfish - The Way Is Through'.

With these 3 powerful energies in mind, it's time to start writing in this journal to unleash the twofold magic within the pages of the LightTool™ that is this 111Magic Journal.

by Joanna Hunter

The Twofold Magic:

1. There is power and pure potential when we write out our dreams. The action of writing is the setting of an intention. Skylar teaches that our intentions are like sacred footprints that pave the way for that energy to enter our lives. Committing your dreams to paper is the first step in owning them and transporting those dreams from the unseen realm into the physical realm of the here and now. Now you can begin to appreciate why so many people freak out at the commitment of writing their dreams down. If your dreams are worthy of you, they are also worthy of being written down.

2. Money loves purpose. We live in a monetary world. We have chosen to incarnate on the planet at a time when we use the currency of money; make peace with this. Sure, there are plenty of free dreams - write those down too. However, many of your dreams will have a monetary cost. The action of writing down your dreams unleashes a little-known money magic spell, that 'money loves purpose'. This journal is perfect for letting money know how you wish to spend it, giving it purpose, and inviting it into your field of consciousness.

Here's the warning:

This 111Magic journal and LightTool™ will change your life if used correctly. Magic is not to be played with. We are only ever given the magic we can handle. Your attitude and intention are everything in magic use!

If, every time you read the journal entries of the 111 experiences and things you desire in this journal and you feel 'bummed,' hard done by, or wondering if you will ever get them, understand this:

You are putting yourself on the frequency of lack, and lack will continue to show up until you learn to place yourself on the frequency of attraction. The frequency of attraction is super simple: joy & gratitude.

Gaze upon the magic of this journal with love, joy, and gratitude and you will come to know real-life magic and what it feels like to live inside your dreams. This LightTool can be used in combination with our gratitude journal LightTool for maximum effect.

The 111Magic Journal is ultimately about creating a life well lived, a life of the extraordinary. I wish to share this magic from Leonardo Da Vinci with you:

"It had long since come to my attention that people of accomplishment rarely sat back and let things happen to them. They went out and happened to things. I have been impressed with the urgency of doing. Knowing is not

enough; we must apply. Being willing is not enough; we must do. As a well spent day brings happy sleep, so a life well spent brings happy death."
– Leonardo Da Vinci

Here's to a life well lived, full of happy memories with the people that matter the most. Happy days followed by happy sleeps. Extraordinary moments that represent a life well lived. When it is our time to be called home to spirit, we can say we lived all out, and created a life of pure magic!

Happy manifesting and intention setting!

Joanna xX

www.joannahunter.com

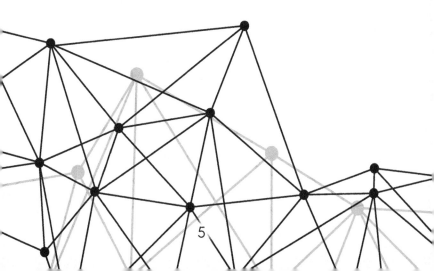

5

111Magic Journal

How 111MAGIC can work for you...

Find yourself a quiet spot, sit with your favourite beverage and take some time to think about all of the things you desire to do.

Write 1 desire for each numbered entry.

As you write each desire down, you begin manifesting this into your reality. You send a powerful signal to the universe that 'This is of your choosing'.

When life gets dull and lacklustre, go to your 111Magic List and find an entry that you would like to do.

Here is some divine inspiration to get you started:

- A place you have always wanted to visit
- Something that scares you
- Something you have always thought looks fun
- A new thing you have always wanted to learn
- A charity you have always wanted to support
- An experience you never thought you would have
- Somewhere local you have always wanted to go but have never got round to it
- Meeting new people
- Indulging a secret obsession
- A spiritual experience you desire to have
- Something that will have you leaving your comfort zone

111MAGIC LIST INDEX

Use this list to record an index of your 111Magic list of dreams and goals for easy referral.

1	☐
2	☐
3	☐
4	☐
5	☐
6	☐
7	☐
8	☐
9	☐
10	☐
11	☐
12	☐
13	☐
14	☐
15	☐
16	☐
17	☐
18	☐
19	☐
20	☐
21	☐
22	☐
23	☐
24	☐
25	☐

Things I want to do with my beautiful & magical life...

26		☐
27		☐
28		☐
29		☐
30		☐
31		☐
32		☐
33		☐
34		☐
35		☐
36		☐
37		☐
38		☐
39		☐
40		☐
41		☐
42		☐
43		☐
44		☐
45		☐
46		☐
47		☐
48		☐
49		☐
50		☐

111Magic List Index continued:

51	☐
52	☐
53	☐
54	☐
55	☐
56	☐
57	☐
58	☐
59	☐
60	☐
61	☐
62	☐
63	☐
64	☐
65	☐
66	☐
67	☐
68	☐
69	☐
70	☐
71	☐
72	☐
73	☐
74	☐
75	☐
76	☐
77	☐
78	☐
79	☐
80	☐

81	☐
82	☐
83	☐
84	☐
85	☐
86	☐
87	☐
88	☐
89	☐
90	☐
91	☐
92	☐
93	☐
94	☐
95	☐
96	☐
97	☐
98	☐
99	☐
100	☐
101	☐
102	☐
103	☐
104	☐
105	☐
106	☐
107	☐
108	☐
109	☐
110	☐
111	☐

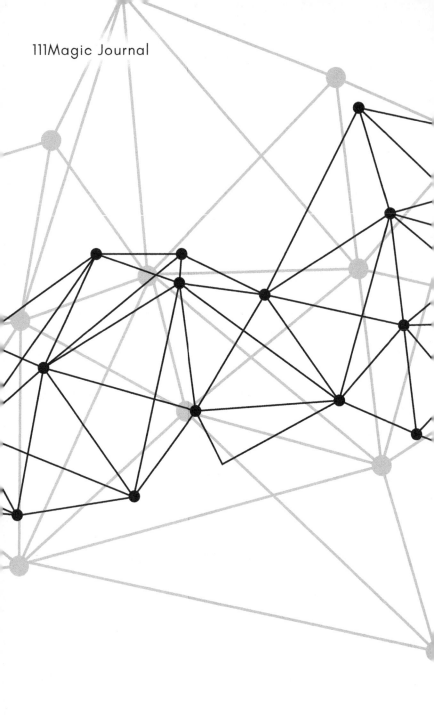

by Joanna Hunter

Creating your
✦ 111MAGIC LIST ✦

Let's make some serious life-magic!

Those who have the courage to dream big are more likely to see their dreams come to fruition.

Dreams are powerful, universal magic that contain energy from the universe inside them. When we have the courage to dream big, to create an honest dialogue with the universe of our deepest desires, we connect with the elemental forces of the universe and we unleash and tap into our creator power.

It is safe for us to dream big, but only when we are willing to remove time from the equation. If it takes you a lifetime to unfold the experiences of your 111Magic List...then it takes a lifetime. But if those dreams are worthy of you, a lifetime will not be too long to wait. So dream the biggest, juiciest, butterfly-inducing dreams that you possibly can.

For additional resources to accompany this journal, check out:-

joannahunter.com/111magicbook

Let's get started...

NO.1 _____

I want to do this because...

_____

_____

_____

_____

_____

_____

_____

Star rating: ☆☆☆☆☆

Date completed:

Who I was with:

The magic:

All the feels:

NO.2 _____

I want to do this because...

_____

_____

_____

_____

_____

_____

_____

_____

_____

Star rating: ☆☆☆☆☆

Date completed:

Who I was with:

The magic:

_____

All the feels:

_____

_____

_____

NO.3

I want to do this because...

_____

_____

_____

_____

_____

_____

_____

_____

_____

Star rating:☆☆☆☆☆

Date completed:
_____

Who I was with:
_____

The magic:
_____

_____

All the feels:
_____

_____

_____

NO.4

I want to do this because...

_____

_____

_____

_____

_____

_____

_____

_____

_____

Star rating: ☆☆☆☆☆

Date completed:

Who I was with:

The magic:

_____

All the feels:

_____

_____

_____

NO.5

I want to do this because...

_____

_____

_____

_____

_____

_____

_____

_____

_____

Star rating:☆☆☆☆☆

Date completed:

Who I was with:

The magic:

All the feels:

NO.6 _____

I want to do this because...

_____

_____

_____

_____

_____

_____

_____

_____

_____

Star rating: ☆☆☆☆☆

Date completed:
_____

Who I was with:
_____

The magic:
_____

_____

All the feels:
_____

_____

_____

_____

NO.7 _____

I want to do this because...

_____

_____

_____

_____

_____

_____

_____

_____

_____

Star rating:☆☆☆☆☆

Date completed: _____

Who I was with: _____

The magic: _____

_____

All the feels: _____

_____

_____

_____

by Joanna Hunter

NO.8 _____

I want to do this because...

_____

_____

_____

_____

_____

_____

_____

_____

_____

Star rating:☆☆☆☆☆

Date completed:
_____

Who I was with:
_____

The magic:
_____

_____

All the feels:
_____

_____

_____

_____

"ON THE OTHER SIDE OF YOUR RESISTANCE ARE ALL THE MIRACLES YOU EVER SOUGHT"

— Skylar

NO.9 _____

I want to do this because...

_____

_____

_____

_____

_____

_____

_____

_____

_____

Star rating:☆☆☆☆☆

Date completed:

_____

Who I was with:

_____

The magic:

_____

_____

All the feels:

_____

_____

_____

NO.10 _____

I want to do this because...

_____

_____

_____

_____

_____

_____

_____

_____

_____

Star rating: ☆☆☆☆☆

Date completed:

_____

Who I was with:

_____

The magic:

_____

_____

All the feels:

_____

_____

_____

_____

NO.11

I want to do this because...

_____

_____

_____

_____

_____

_____

_____

_____

_____

Star rating:☆☆☆☆☆

Date completed:

Who I was with:

The magic:

All the feels:

NO.12 _____

I want to do this because...

_____

_____

_____

_____

_____

_____

_____

_____

Star rating:☆☆☆☆☆

Date completed:
_____

Who I was with:
_____

The magic:
_____

_____

All the feels:
_____

_____

_____

_____

NO.13

I want to do this because...

_____

_____

_____

_____

_____

_____

_____

_____

Star rating:☆☆☆☆☆

Date completed:

_____

Who I was with:

_____

The magic:

_____

_____

All the feels:

_____

_____

_____

by Joanna Hunter

NO.14 _____

I want to do this because...

_____

_____

_____

_____

_____

_____

_____

_____

_____

Star rating: ☆☆☆☆☆

Date completed:

_____

Who I was with:

_____

The magic:

_____

All the feels:

_____

_____

_____

NO.15 _____

I want to do this because...

_____

_____

_____

_____

_____

_____

_____

_____

_____

Star rating:☆☆☆☆☆

Date completed:

Who I was with:

The magic:

_____

All the feels:

_____

_____

_____

NO.16 _____

I want to do this because...

_____

_____

_____

_____

_____

_____

_____

_____

_____

Star rating: ☆☆☆☆☆

Date completed: _____

Who I was with: _____

The magic: _____

_____

All the feels: _____

_____

_____

_____

"You can be laying bricks or you can be building your dream home, the choice is yours."

– SKYLAR

NO.17

I want to do this because...

_____

_____

_____

_____

_____

_____

_____

_____

_____

Star rating:☆☆☆☆☆

Date completed:

Who I was with:

The magic:

All the feels:

NO.18 _____

I want to do this because...

_____

_____

_____

_____

_____

_____

_____

_____

Star rating: ☆☆☆☆☆

Date completed:
_____

Who I was with:
_____

The magic:
_____

_____

All the feels:
_____

_____

_____

_____

111Magic Journal

NO.19

I want to do this because...

_____

_____

_____

_____

_____

_____

_____

_____

_____

Star rating:☆☆☆☆☆

Date completed:

Who I was with:

The magic:

_____

All the feels:

_____

_____

_____

NO.20 _____

I want to do this because...

_____

_____

_____

_____

_____

_____

_____

_____

_____

Star rating:☆☆☆☆☆

Date completed:
_____

Who I was with:
_____

The magic:
_____

_____

All the feels:
_____

_____

_____

_____

NO.21

I want to do this because...

_____

_____

_____

_____

_____

_____

_____

_____

_____

_____

Star rating:☆☆☆☆☆

Date completed: _____

Who I was with: _____

The magic: _____

_____

All the feels: _____

_____

_____

_____

NO.22

I want to do this because...

_____

_____

_____

_____

_____

_____

_____

_____

_____

Star rating:☆☆☆☆☆

Date completed:

Who I was with:

The magic:

All the feels:

NO.23

I want to do this because...

_____

_____

_____

_____

_____

_____

_____

_____

_____

Star rating:☆☆☆☆☆

Date completed:

Who I was with:

The magic:

_____

All the feels:

_____

_____

_____

NO.24

I want to do this because...

_____

_____

_____

_____

_____

_____

_____

_____

_____

Star rating:☆☆☆☆☆

Date completed:
_____

Who I was with:
_____

The magic:
_____

All the feels:
_____

_____

_____

_____

"DESIRES COME FROM THE SOUL. THEY TAKE YOU ON GREAT ADVENTURES INTO THE VERY CORE OF WHO YOU ARE."

— Skylar

NO.25 _____

I want to do this because...

_____

_____

_____

_____

_____

_____

_____

_____

_____

Star rating:☆☆☆☆☆

Date completed: _____

Who I was with: _____

The magic: _____

_____

All the feels: _____

_____

_____

_____

by Joanna Hunter

NO.26 _____

I want to do this because...

_____

_____

_____

_____

_____

_____

_____

_____

_____

Star rating: ☆☆☆☆☆

Date completed:
_____

Who I was with:
_____

The magic:
_____

All the feels:
_____

_____

_____

_____

NO.27 _____

I want to do this because...

_____

_____

_____

_____

_____

_____

_____

_____

Star rating:☆☆☆☆☆

Date completed: _____

Who I was with: _____

The magic: _____

_____

All the feels: _____

_____

_____

_____

NO.28 _____

I want to do this because...

_____

_____

_____

_____

_____

_____

_____

_____

_____

Star rating:☆☆☆☆☆

Date completed:
_____

Who I was with:
_____

The magic:
_____

_____

All the feels:
_____

_____

_____

_____

NO.29

I want to do this because...

_____

_____

_____

_____

_____

_____

_____

_____

Star rating:☆☆☆☆☆

Date completed:
_____

Who I was with:
_____

The magic:
_____

_____

All the feels:
_____

_____

_____

by Joanna Hunter

NO.30 _____

I want to do this because...

_____

_____

_____

_____

_____

_____

_____

_____

_____

Star rating: ☆☆☆☆☆

Date completed:

Who I was with:

The magic:

_____

All the feels:

_____

_____

_____

NO.31

I want to do this because...

_____

_____

_____

_____

_____

_____

_____

_____

Star rating:☆☆☆☆☆

Date completed:
_____

Who I was with:
_____

The magic:
_____

_____

All the feels:
_____

_____

_____

NO.32 _____

I want to do this because...

_____

_____

_____

_____

_____

_____

_____

_____

_____

Star rating: ☆☆☆☆☆

Date completed:
_____

Who I was with:
_____

The magic:
_____

_____

All the feels:
_____

_____

_____

_____

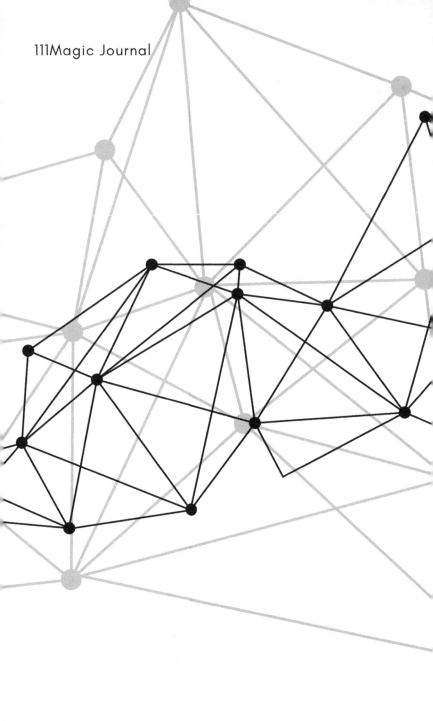

"Every day is an opportunity to live your dreams out loud."

– JOANNA HUNTER

NO.33 _____

I want to do this because...

_____

_____

_____

_____

_____

_____

_____

_____

Star rating:☆☆☆☆☆

Date completed:

_____

Who I was with:

_____

The magic:

_____

All the feels:

_____

_____

_____

_____

NO.34 _____

I want to do this because...

_____

_____

_____

_____

_____

_____

_____

_____

Star rating:☆☆☆☆☆

Date completed:
_____

Who I was with:
_____

The magic:
_____

_____

All the feels:
_____

_____

_____

_____

NO.35

I want to do this because...

_____

_____

_____

_____

_____

_____

_____

_____

_____

Star rating:☆☆☆☆☆

Date completed:

Who I was with:

The magic:

All the feels:

NO.36 _____

I want to do this because...

_____

_____

_____

_____

_____

_____

_____

_____

_____

Star rating:☆☆☆☆☆

Date completed:
_____

Who I was with:
_____

The magic:
_____

_____

All the feels:
_____

_____

_____

NO.37

I want to do this because...

_____

_____

_____

_____

_____

_____

_____

_____

_____

Star rating:☆☆☆☆☆

Date completed:

Who I was with:

The magic:

All the feels:

NO.38 _____

I want to do this because...

_____

_____

_____

_____

_____

_____

_____

_____

_____

Star rating:☆☆☆☆☆

Date completed:
_____

Who I was with:
_____

The magic:
_____

_____

All the feels:
_____

_____

_____

_____

NO.39

I want to do this because...

_____

_____

_____

_____

_____

_____

_____

_____

Star rating:☆☆☆☆☆

Date completed:

Who I was with:

The magic:

All the feels:

by Joanna Hunter

NO.40 _____

I want to do this because...

_____

_____

_____

_____

_____

_____

_____

_____

_____

Star rating: ☆☆☆☆☆

Date completed:

_____

Who I was with:

_____

The magic:

_____

_____

All the feels:

_____

_____

_____

_____

"WITH VISION, MISSION & PURPOSE YOU CAN ACHIEVE ANYTHING."

– Joanna Hunter

NO.41

I want to do this because...

_____

_____

_____

_____

_____

_____

_____

_____

_____

Star rating:☆☆☆☆☆

Date completed:

Who I was with:

The magic:

All the feels:

NO.42

I want to do this because...

_____

_____

_____

_____

_____

_____

_____

_____

_____

Star rating: ☆☆☆☆☆

Date completed:

_____

Who I was with:

_____

The magic:

_____

All the feels:

_____

_____

_____

NO.43 _____

I want to do this because...

_____

_____

_____

_____

_____

_____

_____

_____

_____

Star rating:☆☆☆☆☆

Date completed:
_____

Who I was with:
_____

The magic:
_____

_____

All the feels:
_____

_____

_____

_____

NO.44 _____

I want to do this because...

_____

_____

_____

_____

_____

_____

_____

_____

_____

Star rating: ☆☆☆☆☆

Date completed:
_____

Who I was with:
_____

The magic:
_____

_____

All the feels:
_____

_____

_____

_____

NO.45

I want to do this because...

_____

_____

_____

_____

_____

_____

_____

_____

_____

Star rating:☆☆☆☆☆

Date completed:

Who I was with:

The magic:

_____

All the feels:

_____

_____

_____

by Joanna Hunter

NO.46 _____

I want to do this because...

_____

_____

_____

_____

_____

_____

_____

_____

_____

Star rating: ☆☆☆☆☆

Date completed:
_____

Who I was with:
_____

The magic:
_____

_____

All the feels:
_____

_____

_____

NO.47

I want to do this because...

_____

_____

_____

_____

_____

_____

_____

_____

_____

Star rating:☆☆☆☆☆

Date completed:

Who I was with:

The magic:

All the feels:

NO.48 _____

I want to do this because...

_____

_____

_____

_____

_____

_____

_____

_____

Star rating:☆☆☆☆☆

Date completed:
_____

Who I was with:
_____

The magic:
_____

_____

All the feels:
_____

_____

_____

_____

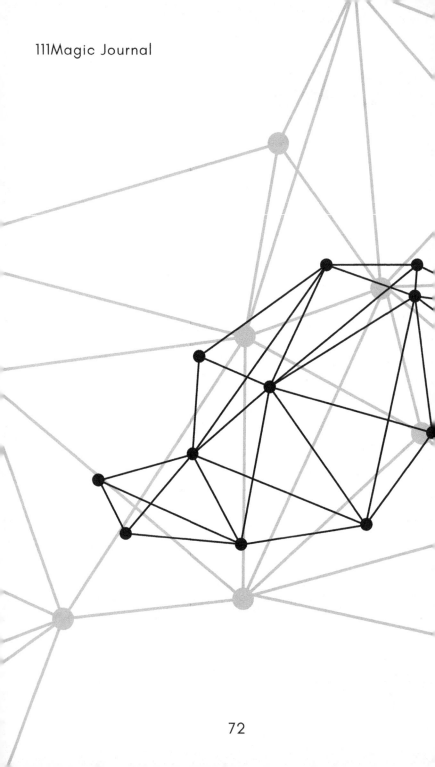

"BET ON YOURSELF AND GO ALL IN! HALF-ASSED WON'T CUT IT."

— Joanna Hunter

NO.49 _____

I want to do this because...

_____

_____

_____

_____

_____

_____

_____

_____

_____

Star rating:☆☆☆☆☆

Date completed:
_____

Who I was with:
_____

The magic:
_____

_____

All the feels:
_____

_____

_____

_____

NO.50 _____

I want to do this because...

_____

_____

_____

_____

_____

_____

_____

_____

_____

Star rating:☆☆☆☆☆

Date completed:
_____

Who I was with:
_____

The magic:
_____

_____

All the feels:
_____

_____

_____

NO.51 _____

I want to do this because...

_____

_____

_____

_____

_____

_____

_____

_____

Star rating:☆☆☆☆☆

Date completed:

Who I was with:

The magic:

_____

All the feels:

_____

_____

_____

by Joanna Hunter

NO.52 _____

I want to do this because...

_____

_____

_____

_____

_____

_____

_____

_____

_____

Star rating:☆☆☆☆☆

Date completed:
_____

Who I was with:
_____

The magic:
_____

_____

All the feels:
_____

_____

_____

_____

NO.53

I want to do this because...

_____

_____

_____

_____

_____

_____

_____

_____

_____

Star rating:☆☆☆☆☆

Date completed:

Who I was with:

The magic:

All the feels:

NO.54 _____

I want to do this because...

_____

_____

_____

_____

_____

_____

_____

_____

_____

Star rating:☆☆☆☆☆

Date completed:

_____

Who I was with:

_____

The magic:

_____

_____

All the feels:

_____

_____

_____

_____

NO.55 _____

I want to do this because...

_____

_____

_____

_____

_____

_____

_____

_____

_____

Star rating:☆☆☆☆☆

Date completed:

_____

Who I was with:

_____

The magic:

_____

_____

All the feels:

_____

_____

_____

NO.56 _____

I want to do this because...

_____

_____

_____

_____

_____

_____

_____

_____

_____

_____

Star rating: ☆☆☆☆☆

Date completed:
_____

Who I was with:
_____

The magic:
_____

_____

All the feels:
_____

_____

_____

_____

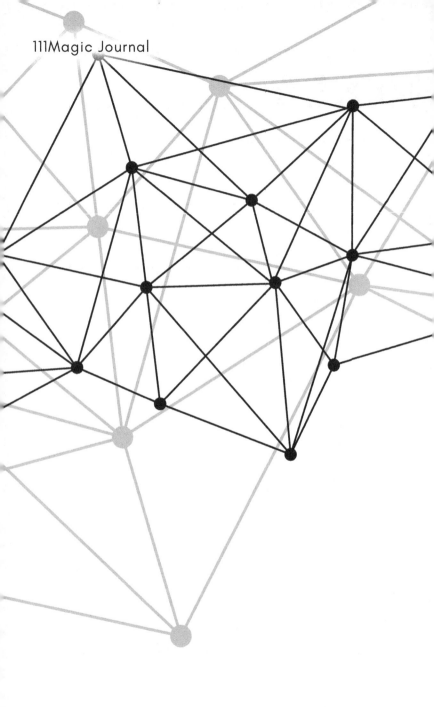

By embracing your spiritual truth, you are stepping into the portal of your soul – let it take you on grand adventures.

- JOANNA HUNTER

NO.57 _____

I want to do this because...

_____

_____

_____

_____

_____

_____

_____

_____

Star rating:☆☆☆☆☆

Date completed:

Who I was with:

The magic:

All the feels:

NO.58

I want to do this because...

_____

_____

_____

_____

_____

_____

_____

_____

_____

Star rating:☆☆☆☆☆

Date completed:

_____

Who I was with:

_____

The magic:

_____

_____

All the feels:

_____

_____

_____

_____

NO.59

I want to do this because...

_____

_____

_____

_____

_____

_____

_____

_____

Star rating:☆☆☆☆☆

Date completed:
_____

Who I was with:
_____

The magic:
_____

All the feels:
_____

_____

_____

NO.60 _____

I want to do this because...

_____

_____

_____

_____

_____

_____

_____

_____

_____

Star rating:☆☆☆☆☆

Date completed:

_____

Who I was with:

_____

The magic:

_____

_____

All the feels:

_____

_____

_____

_____

NO.61

I want to do this because...

_____

_____

_____

_____

_____

_____

_____

_____

Star rating: ☆☆☆☆☆

Date completed:
_____

Who I was with:
_____

The magic:
_____

_____

All the feels:
_____

_____

_____

by Joanna Hunter

NO.62 _____

I want to do this because...

_____

_____

_____

_____

_____

_____

_____

_____

Star rating: ☆☆☆☆☆

Date completed:

_____

Who I was with:

_____

The magic:

_____

_____

All the feels:

_____

_____

_____

NO.63

I want to do this because...

_____

_____

_____

_____

_____

_____

_____

_____

Star rating:☆☆☆☆☆

Date completed:
_____

Who I was with:
_____

The magic:
_____

_____

All the feels:
_____

_____

_____

_____

by Joanna Hunter

NO.64 _____

I want to do this because...

_____

_____

_____

_____

_____

_____

_____

_____

_____

Star rating:☆☆☆☆☆

Date completed:
_____

Who I was with:
_____

The magic:
_____

_____

All the feels:
_____

_____

_____

_____

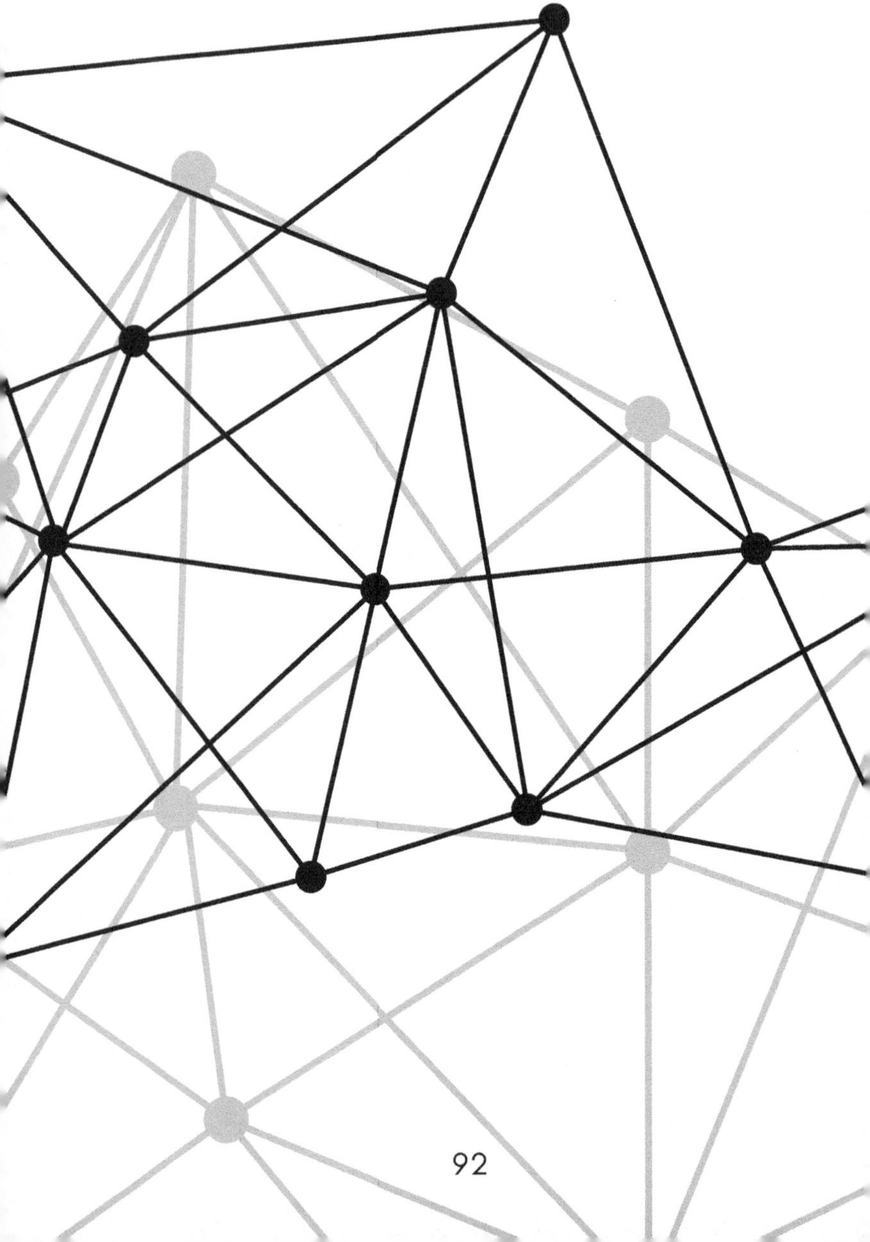

"THERE IS NO PATH TO HAPPINESS. HAPPINESS IS THE PATH."

— *Buddha*

NO.65 _____

I want to do this because...

_____

_____

_____

_____

_____

_____

_____

_____

Star rating:☆☆☆☆☆

Date completed:
_____

Who I was with:
_____

The magic:
_____

_____

All the feels:
_____

_____

_____

_____

NO.66 _____

I want to do this because...

_____

_____

_____

_____

_____

_____

_____

_____

_____

Star rating:☆☆☆☆☆

Date completed:

_____

Who I was with:

_____

The magic:

_____

_____

All the feels:

_____

_____

_____

_____

NO.67

I want to do this because...

_____

_____

_____

_____

_____

_____

_____

_____

Star rating:☆☆☆☆☆

Date completed:

_____

Who I was with:

_____

The magic:

_____

_____

All the feels:

_____

_____

_____

_____

by Joanna Hunter

NO.68 _____

I want to do this because...

_____

_____

_____

_____

_____

_____

_____

_____

_____

Star rating: ☆☆☆☆☆

Date completed:
_____

Who I was with:
_____

The magic:
_____

_____

All the feels:
_____

_____

_____

_____

NO.69

I want to do this because...

_____

_____

_____

_____

_____

_____

_____

_____

_____

Star rating:☆☆☆☆☆

Date completed:

Who I was with:

The magic:

All the feels:

NO.70 _____

I want to do this because...

_____

_____

_____

_____

_____

_____

_____

_____

Star rating:☆☆☆☆☆

Date completed:

Who I was with:

The magic:

_____

All the feels:

_____

_____

_____

NO.71

I want to do this because...

_____

_____

_____

_____

_____

_____

_____

_____

Star rating:☆☆☆☆☆

Date completed:
_____

Who I was with:
_____

The magic:
_____

_____

All the feels:
_____

_____

_____

_____

by Joanna Hunter

NO.72 _____

I want to do this because...

_____

_____

_____

_____

_____

_____

_____

_____

_____

Star rating:☆☆☆☆☆

Date completed:
_____

Who I was with:
_____

The magic:
_____

_____

All the feels:
_____

_____

_____

_____

111Magic Journal

by Joanna Hunter

Make your life a good-vibes-only zone.

NO.73 _____

I want to do this because...

_____

_____

_____

_____

_____

_____

_____

_____

Star rating:☆☆☆☆☆

Date completed:
_____

Who I was with:
_____

The magic:
_____

_____

All the feels:
_____

_____

_____

_____

NO.74 _____

I want to do this because...

_____

_____

_____

_____

_____

_____

_____

_____

_____

Star rating: ☆☆☆☆☆

Date completed: _____

Who I was with: _____

The magic: _____

_____

All the feels: _____

_____

_____

_____

NO.75 _____

I want to do this because...

_____

_____

_____

_____

_____

_____

_____

_____

_____

_____

Star rating:☆☆☆☆☆

Date completed:
_____

Who I was with:
_____

The magic:
_____

_____

All the feels:
_____

_____

_____

_____

NO.76 _____

I want to do this because...

_____

_____

_____

_____

_____

_____

_____

_____

_____

Star rating:☆☆☆☆☆

Date completed:
_____

Who I was with:
_____

The magic:
_____

_____

All the feels:
_____

_____

_____

_____

NO.77 _____

I want to do this because...

_____

_____

_____

_____

_____

_____

_____

_____

Star rating:☆☆☆☆☆

Date completed:

_____

Who I was with:

_____

The magic:

_____

_____

All the feels:

_____

_____

_____

_____

NO.78 _____

I want to do this because...

_____

_____

_____

_____

_____

_____

_____

_____

_____

Star rating: ☆☆☆☆☆

Date completed:
_____

Who I was with:
_____

The magic:
_____

_____

All the feels:
_____

_____

_____

_____

NO.79 _____

I want to do this because...

_____

_____

_____

_____

_____

_____

_____

_____

Star rating:☆☆☆☆☆

Date completed:
_____

Who I was with:
_____

The magic:
_____

_____

All the feels:
_____

_____

_____

NO.80 _____

I want to do this because...

_____

_____

_____

_____

_____

_____

_____

_____

Star rating:☆☆☆☆☆

Date completed:

_____

Who I was with:

_____

The magic:

_____

_____

All the feels:

_____

_____

_____

_____

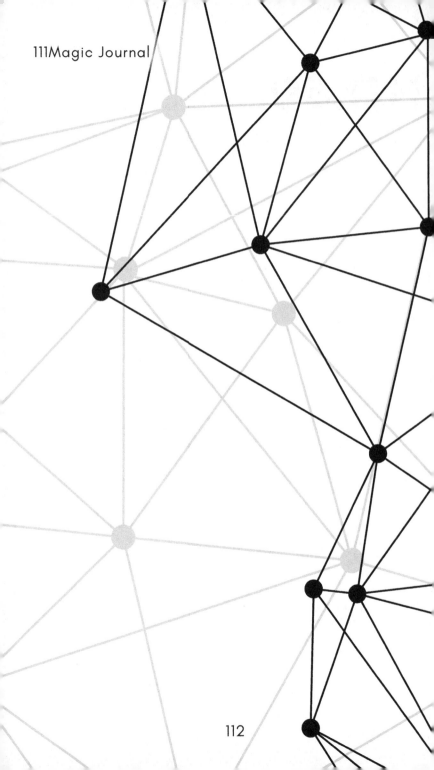

TRAVEL FEEDS THE MIND, FILLS YOUR SOUL AND LEAVES YOU RICHER.

– Joanna Hunter

NO.81 _____

I want to do this because...

_____

_____

_____

_____

_____

_____

_____

_____

_____

Star rating:☆☆☆☆☆

Date completed:
_____

Who I was with:
_____

The magic:
_____

_____

All the feels:
_____

_____

_____

_____

NO.82

I want to do this because...

_____

_____

_____

_____

_____

_____

_____

_____

_____

Star rating: ☆☆☆☆☆

Date completed:

Who I was with:

The magic:

All the feels:

NO.83

I want to do this because...

_____

_____

_____

_____

_____

_____

_____

_____

_____

Star rating:☆☆☆☆☆

Date completed:
_____

Who I was with:
_____

The magic:
_____

_____

All the feels:
_____

_____

_____

_____

NO.84 _____

I want to do this because...

_____

_____

_____

_____

_____

_____

_____

_____

_____

_____

Star rating: ☆☆☆☆☆

Date completed:

_____

Who I was with:

_____

The magic:

_____

_____

All the feels:

_____

_____

_____

NO.85

I want to do this because...

_____

_____

_____

_____

_____

_____

_____

_____

Star rating:☆☆☆☆☆

Date completed:

Who I was with:

The magic:

All the feels:

NO.86 _____

I want to do this because...

_____

_____

_____

_____

_____

_____

_____

_____

Star rating:☆☆☆☆☆

Date completed:
_____

Who I was with:
_____

The magic:
_____

_____

All the feels:
_____

_____

_____

_____

NO.87

I want to do this because...

_____

_____

_____

_____

_____

_____

_____

_____

_____

Star rating:☆☆☆☆☆

Date completed:

Who I was with:

The magic:

All the feels:

NO.88

I want to do this because...

_____

_____

_____

_____

_____

_____

_____

_____

_____

Star rating: ☆☆☆☆☆

Date completed:
_____

Who I was with:
_____

The magic:
_____

_____

All the feels:
_____

_____

_____

_____

By Joanna Hunter

"Your next adventure won't be found in your comfort zone."

NO.89

I want to do this because...

_____

_____

_____

_____

_____

_____

_____

_____

Star rating:☆☆☆☆☆

Date completed:
_____

Who I was with:
_____

The magic:
_____

_____

All the feels:
_____

_____

_____

_____

by Joanna Hunter

NO.90 _____

I want to do this because...

_____

_____

_____

_____

_____

_____

_____

_____

_____

Star rating: ☆☆☆☆☆

Date completed:
_____

Who I was with:
_____

The magic:
_____

_____

All the feels:
_____

_____

_____

_____

NO.91 _____

I want to do this because...

_____

_____

_____

_____

_____

_____

_____

_____

_____

Star rating:☆☆☆☆☆

Date completed:
_____

Who I was with:
_____

The magic:
_____

_____

All the feels:
_____

_____

_____

NO.92 _____

I want to do this because...

_____

_____

_____

_____

_____

_____

_____

_____

_____

Star rating:☆☆☆☆☆

Date completed:
_____

Who I was with:
_____

The magic:
_____

_____

All the feels:
_____

_____

_____

_____

NO.93 _____

I want to do this because...

_____

_____

_____

_____

_____

_____

_____

_____

Star rating:☆☆☆☆☆

Date completed:

Who I was with:

The magic:

_____

All the feels:

_____

_____

_____

by Joanna Hunter

NO.94 _____

I want to do this because...

_____

_____

_____

_____

_____

_____

_____

_____

_____

Star rating: ☆☆☆☆☆

Date completed:
_____

Who I was with:
_____

The magic:
_____

_____

All the feels:
_____

_____

_____

_____

NO.95

I want to do this because...

_____

_____

_____

_____

_____

_____

_____

_____

_____

Star rating:☆☆☆☆☆

Date completed:

Who I was with:

The magic:

_____

All the feels:

_____

_____

_____

NO.96 _____

I want to do this because...

_____

_____

_____

_____

_____

_____

_____

_____

Star rating: ☆☆☆☆☆

Date completed:
_____

Who I was with:
_____

The magic:
_____

_____

All the feels:
_____

_____

_____

_____

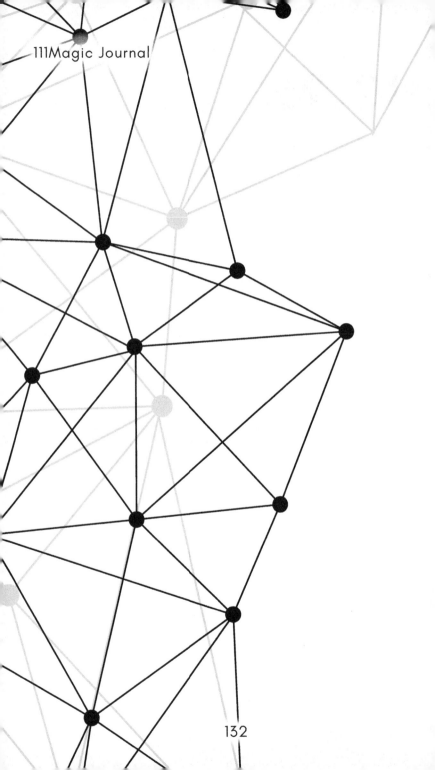

IF THE PLAN DOESN'T WORK, CHANGE THE PLAN, BUT NEVER THE GOAL.

NO.97

I want to do this because...

_____

_____

_____

_____

_____

_____

_____

_____

_____

Star rating:☆☆☆☆☆

Date completed:

_____

Who I was with:

_____

The magic:

_____

_____

All the feels:

_____

_____

_____

by Joanna Hunter

NO.98 _____

I want to do this because...

_____

_____

_____

_____

_____

_____

_____

_____

Star rating:☆☆☆☆☆

Date completed:

_____

Who I was with:

_____

The magic:

_____

All the feels:

_____

_____

_____

_____

NO.99 _____

I want to do this because...

_____

_____

_____

_____

_____

_____

_____

_____

Star rating:☆☆☆☆☆

Date completed:
_____

Who I was with:
_____

The magic:
_____

_____

All the feels:
_____

_____

_____

NO.100 _____

I want to do this because...

_____

_____

_____

_____

_____

_____

_____

_____

_____

Star rating: ☆☆☆☆☆

Date completed: _____

Who I was with: _____

The magic: _____

_____

All the feels: _____

_____

_____

_____

NO.101

I want to do this because...

_____

_____

_____

_____

_____

_____

_____

_____

_____

Star rating:☆☆☆☆☆

Date completed:

_____

Who I was with:

_____

The magic:

_____

All the feels:

_____

_____

_____

NO.102_____

I want to do this because...

_____

_____

_____

_____

_____

_____

_____

_____

_____

Star rating:☆☆☆☆☆

Date completed:
_____

Who I was with:
_____

The magic:
_____

_____

All the feels:
_____

_____

_____

_____

NO.103 _____

I want to do this because...

_____

_____

_____

_____

_____

_____

_____

_____

Star rating: ☆☆☆☆☆

Date completed:

_____

Who I was with:

_____

The magic:

_____

_____

All the feels:

_____

_____

_____

NO.104 _____

I want to do this because...

_____

_____

_____

_____

_____

_____

_____

_____

_____

Star rating: ☆☆☆☆☆

Date completed:

_____

Who I was with:

_____

The magic:

_____

_____

All the feels:

_____

_____

_____

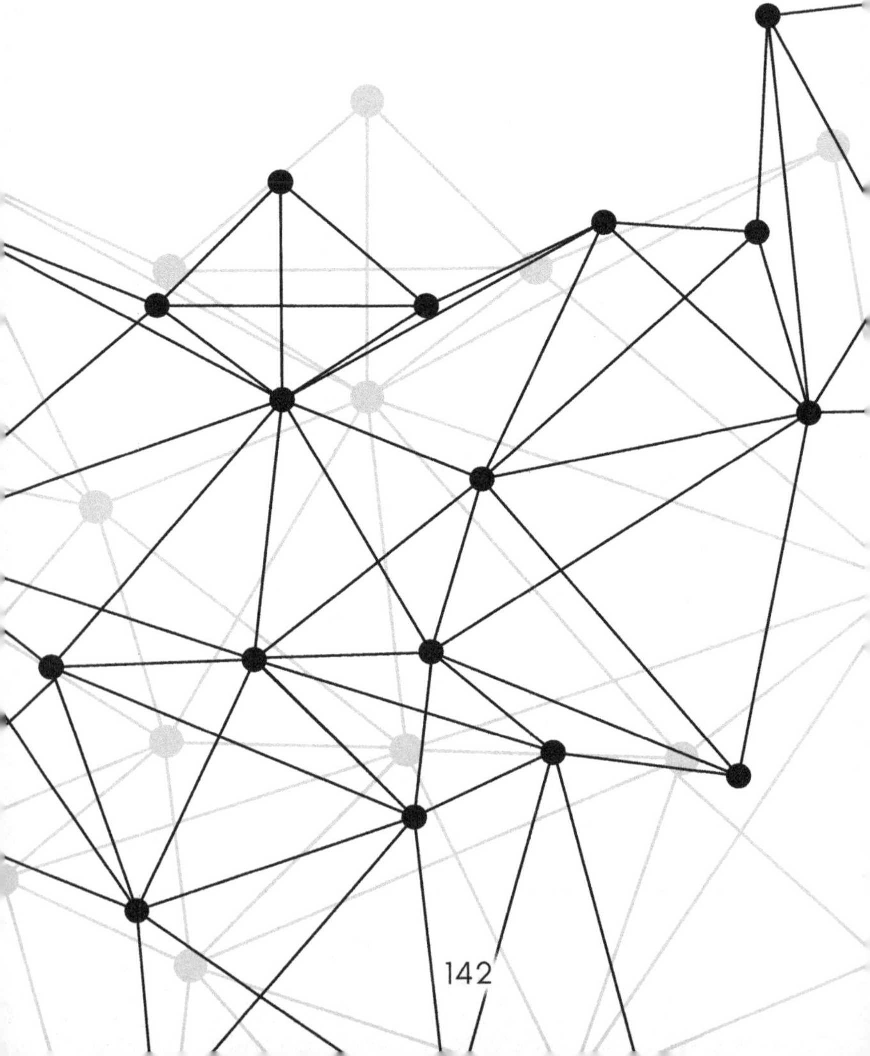

Every single day, do an increment that brings your closer to your goals.

– JOANNA HUNTER

NO.105

I want to do this because...

_____

_____

_____

_____

_____

_____

_____

_____

Star rating: ☆☆☆☆☆

Date completed:

Who I was with:

The magic:

_____

All the feels:

_____

_____

_____

NO.106 _____

I want to do this because...

_____

_____

_____

_____

_____

_____

_____

_____

_____

Star rating:☆☆☆☆☆

Date completed:
_____

Who I was with:
_____

The magic:
_____

_____

All the feels:
_____

_____

_____

_____

NO.107 _____

I want to do this because...

_____

_____

_____

_____

_____

_____

_____

_____

Star rating:☆☆☆☆☆

Date completed:

Who I was with:

The magic:

All the feels:

NO.108 _____

I want to do this because...

_____

_____

_____

_____

_____

_____

_____

_____

Star rating:☆☆☆☆☆

Date completed:
_____

Who I was with:
_____

The magic:
_____

_____

All the feels:
_____

_____

_____

_____

NO.109 _____

I want to do this because...

_____

_____

_____

_____

_____

_____

_____

_____

_____

Star rating:☆☆☆☆☆

Date completed:

Who I was with:

The magic:

All the feels:

NO.110 _____

I want to do this because...

_____

_____

_____

_____

_____

_____

_____

_____

_____

Star rating: ☆☆☆☆☆

Date completed: _____

Who I was with: _____

The magic: _____

_____

All the feels: _____

_____

_____

_____

NO.111

I want to do this because...

_____

_____

_____

_____

_____

_____

_____

_____

Star rating: ☆☆☆☆☆

Date completed:

Who I was with:

The magic:

All the feels:

by Joanna Hunter

THE ROOTS OF ALL GOODNESS LIE IN THE SOIL OF APPRECIATION FOR GOODNESS.

SUMMARY

I completed my 111Magic List on...

_____

It took me: DAYS   MTHS   YRS

Knowing I have done 111 things for myself, I feel...

_____

_____

_____

I must do number _____ again because...

_____

_____

_____

The most important thing I learned was...

_____

_____

_____

My favourite place was...

_____

_____

_____

I'll never forget as long as I live...

_____

_____

_____

_____

by Joanna Hunter

The funnest item on my list was...

_____

_____

_____

This friend did the most adventures with me...

_____

_____

_____

What was I thinking when I did...

_____

_____

_____

This one didn't live up to expectations...

_____

This was by far the most awkward one...

_____

My favourite advice going forward is...

_____

My biggest splurge was...

_____

I was so scared when...

_____

I am most proud of...

_____

The most rewarding...

The strangest...

The hardest...

The most sensual...

The craziest...

Took the longest...

Was the shortest...

Felt messed up...

The most hilarious...

The most mentally challenging...

The most physically challenging...

The most delightful...

The most spiritual...

Notes

by Joanna Hunter

JOURNAL

A snapshot of where I am at right now as I start this journey...

_____

_____

_____

_____

_____

_____

_____

_____

_____

_____

_____

_____

_____

_____

_____

_____

_____

_____

_____

_____

JOURNAL

Where I am now that I have completed this journey...

_____

_____

_____

_____

_____

_____

_____

_____

_____

_____

_____

_____

_____

_____

_____

_____

_____

_____

_____

_____

_____

_____

by Joanna Hunter

JOURNAL

My plans for the future...

_____

_____

_____

_____

_____

_____

_____

_____

_____

_____

_____

_____

_____

_____

_____

_____

_____

_____

_____

_____

NOTES

NOTES

NOTES

_____

_____

_____

_____

_____

_____

_____

_____

_____

_____

_____

_____

_____

_____

_____

_____

_____

_____

_____

_____

NOTES

NOTES

✧ 111MAGIC LIST ✧

Life is for living, for embarking on exciting adventures, living your dreams out loud, accomplishing your goals and creating a life of your deepest desires.

This journal will turn into a beautiful keepsake of a life well-lived, filled with wonderful memories and capturing the moments your dreams became reality.

About The Author

@joannahuntercom

Joanna Hunter is an author, clairvoyant medium, spiritual life & business coach, channel for a collective consciousness called Skylar and the High Priestess of the LightWeb - a soul-based technology that will change your life.

Joanna lives in the magical Highlands of Scotland, near standing stones and mystical places with hubby, her children and her Jack Russell called Daisy. When she's not teaching online, she is creating live events and retreats for her global community, taking them to sacred places both within themselves and in the outer world.

The 111Magic Journal is a LightTool™ which supports Joanna and her spirit team's work with LightWeb, BeMagic and teaching the Codex of Light, helping humanity shed 'lack' of consciousness and move into deeper Source alignment and Magic!

As a lifelong medium and psychic Joanna's love of self-enrichment knows no bounds, she has been a spiritual teacher since she was just 23 years old and now has over two decades of experience in teaching and sharing wisdom of Source, with her spirit team Skylar. Joanna has helped hundreds of spiritual entrepreneurs create impact-making businesses with the philosophy of no hustle ever! Teaching others ease, joy, and flow via her Source-downloaded courses, live events and books.

For more information visit :-
www.joannahunter.com/books

Made in the USA
Coppell, TX
03 December 2022